HOORAY!

_____

can read this book!

In this story, you will read or hear words with the **short a** vowel sound. Look for these words in the story and sound them out:

after	at	bad	ball
bat	fast	had	hat
Jan	mad	Matt	Pam
plan	ran	Sam	tag
tagged	whack	whacked	

Here are some sight words:

a	blue	how	little
showed	the	to	was

Here are some fun Berenstain Bears words:

Brother   **played**   **Sister**

Brother Bear showed little cubs how to hold a bat.

Sister Bear showed how to
whack the ball.

Matt with a red hat was
up at bat.

Oops!

Matt had a bad hit.

Pam whacked the ball!

She ran fast.

Pam ran and ran.

Brother Bear ran to get Pam.

Sam in a blue hat tagged Pam.

Then Sam ran!

Pam ran after Sam.

Sam ran after Jan.

Everyone played tag!

Brother was mad!

This was not the plan!

I CAN READ!™ with the BERENSTAIN BEARS

by Jan and Mike Berenstain

Phonics scope and sequence by Cathy Toohey

HOORAY!

_____

can read this book!

In this story, you will read or hear words with the **short e** vowel sound. Look for these words in the story and sound them out:

bent	felt	help
let's	mess	pen
red	sell	selling
well		

Here are some sight words:

a	have	is	it
our	the	we	

Here are some fun Berenstain Bears words:

clean	home	Mama
teddy bear		

Our home is a mess!

We help Mama clean.

Let's have a yard sale.

Let's sell our old stuff.

Let's sell the bent pole.

It still works well.

Let's sell the teddy bear.

He's not looking well.

Look at this spot from a red pen.

Do you think it will sell?

We felt sad selling
our stuff.

No yard sale today!

I CAN READ!™ with the BERENSTAIN BEARS

by Jan and Mike Berenstain

Phonics scope and sequence by Cathy Toohey

I Can Read! Phonics

The Berenstain Bears®

THE HIPMUNK

Book 3 · Short i

HOORAY!

_____

can read this book!

In this story, you will read or hear words
with the **short i** vowel sound. Look for these
words in the story and sound them out:

big	**chipmunk**	**did**
give	**gives**	**him**
his	**in**	**is**
it	**live**	**milk**
Sister	**with**	

Here are some sight words:

a	**come**	**he**	**keep**
sees	**she**	**the**	**to**
wants	**we**	**where**	

Here are some fun Berenstain Bears words:

friends	**Mama**	**trouble**

Sister sees a chipmunk.

Sister wants to keep him.

The chipmunk needs his mother

He cannot live with us.

Where is Mother Chipmunk?

She did not come.

Mama gives the chipmunk milk.

We give him a bed.

The chipmunk gets in
BIG trouble.

It is time for the chipmunk
to be with his friends.

I CAN READ!™ with the BERENSTAIN BEARS

by Jan and Mike Berenstain

Phonics scope and sequence by Cathy Toohey

I Can Read! Phonics

The Berenstain Bears

IT'S NOT A FROG

Book 4 • Short o

HOORAY!

_____

can read this book!

In this story, you will read or hear words with the **short o** vowel sound. Look for these words in the story and sound them out:

along	**bops**	**cotton**
dog	**forgot**	**frog**
got	**hot**	**not**
pond	**rock**	**stops**

Here are some sight words:

a	**about**	**from**	**sees**
the	**they**	**to**	**want**
wants	**would**		

Here are some fun Berenstain Bears words:

Brother	**cubs**	**kitten**
Mama		

Brother wants the frog.

The frog is on a rock.

Brother stops.

He sees a kitten in the pond.

Brother shows what he got
from the pond.
It is not a frog.
It is a kitten!

Mama cleans the kitten
with cotton and hot water.

The cubs want to keep the kitten.

But they forgot about their dog.

They do not get along!

Kitten bops the dog.

A frog would have been a

better pet.

I CAN READ!™ with the
BERENSTAIN BEARS

by Jan and Mike Berenstain

Phonics scope and sequence by Cathy Toohey

THE FUNNY PUP

Book 5 · Short u

HOORAY!

_____

can read this book!

In this story, you will read or hear words with the **short u** vowel sound. Look for these words in the story and sound them out:

but	**cubs**	**funny**
hugs	**pup**	**pup's**
pups	**rub**	**tummy**

Here are some sight words:

get	**go**	**one**	**see**
the	**to**	**want**	**wants**
with			

Here are some fun Berenstain Bears words:

eggs	**farm**	**Mama**
sign	**Sister**	

The cubs go with Mama
to get eggs at the farm.

The cubs see a sign:

Pups for Sale!

But Mama wants eggs,

not pups.

One funny pup rolls over.
Sister wants to rub the
pup's tummy.

The cubs want the funny pup,
but Mama wants eggs.

Mama holds the pup.

Mama hugs the pup.

They go home with eggs
and the funny pup!

I CAN READ!™ with the BERENSTAIN BEARS

by Jan and Mike Berenstain

Phonics scope and sequence by Cathy Toohey

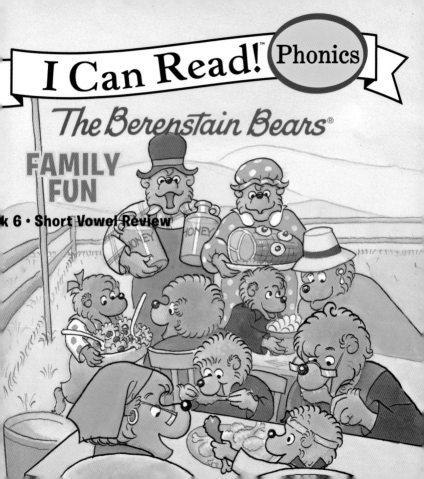

HOORAY!

_____

can read this book!

In this story, you will read or hear words with the short vowel sounds. Look for these words in the story and sound them out.

short a:

a	Gramps	Gran	pass
path	party	that's	yard

short e:

get	help	next	pedal	sets

short i:

drink	in	is	isn't	it
it's	kiss	sing	twins	with

short o:

hot	lot	not

short u:

cubs	fun	Gus	hug
jug	much	run	sun
uncle	uncles	up	

The sun is up.

The day is hot.

The Bears get ready for a big family party.

Papa sets up the yard.

The cubs help Mama with food
and drink.

Is it too much?

No, it isn't!

Up the path run Gramps and

Gran, aunts and uncles . . .

and that's not all!

Next, the twins pedal in.

There's Uncle Gus!

They hug.

They kiss.

They pass around the

honey jug!

They dance.

They sing.

They eat a lot.

It's fun to be with family.

I CAN READ!™ with the BERENSTAIN BEARS

by Jan and Mike Berenstain

Phonics scope and sequence by Cathy Toohey

I Can Read! Phonics

The Berenstain Bears®

RANCH
VACATION

Book 7 • Long a

HOORAY!

_____

can read this book!

In this story, you will read or hear words with the **long a** vowel sounds. Look for these words in the story and sound them out:

afraid	away	brave
great	mane	name
neigh	okay	plane
sails	stay	takes
vacation	way	

Here are some sight words:

are	going	of
says	to	wants

Here are some fun Berenstain Bears words:

cowboy	family	ouch
ranch	ride	Tex
uncle		

The Bear family is going on

vacation out west.

A plane takes them up and

away.

Uncle Tex is at the ranch.

He wears a cowboy hat.

Red is the name of a great,
big horse with a yellow mane.
Red is way too big for the cubs.

Papa wants to ride Red.

He is brave.

Mama and the cubs are
afraid.

"Neigh," says Red.

Uh-oh! Papa sails through the air. Ouch!

Their stay comes to an end.

Papa feels okay.

Up, up, and away goes the plane

I CAN READ!™ with the BERENSTAIN BEARS

by Jan and Mike Berenstain

Phonics scope and sequence by Cathy Toohey

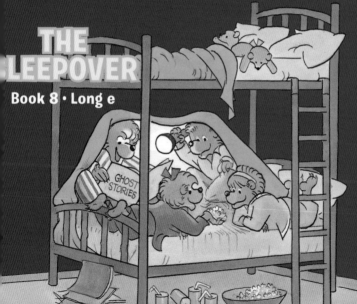

I Can Read! Phonics

The Berenstain Bears

THE SLEEPOVER

Book 8 · Long e

HOORAY!

_____

can read this book!

In this story, you will read or hear words with the **long e** vowel sound. Look for these words in the story and sound them out:

beats	**dreams**	**eat**
feet	**heap**	**leap**
movie	**peek**	**read**
really	**shriek**	**sleep**
sleepover	**sweet**	**teeth**
treats	**tree**	

Here are some sight words:

are	**now**	**the**
they	**watch**	**will**

Here are some fun Berenstain Bears words:

game	**house**	**play**
pretend	**spooky**	**stories**

Sister and Brother are having

a sleepover at the tree house.

Will they get much sleep?

They eat dinner.

Lizzy beats them at a game.

They watch a movie.

Are they ready
to sleep?
No!

They leap.

They tickle feet.

They play in a heap.

Are they ready to sleep?

No!

They brush teeth.

Mama and Papa read.

Sweet dreams.

The cubs go to sleep . . . but not really!

Spooky stories make the girls shriek.

They pretend to sleep when Mama and Papa peek in.

Now the cubs eat treats.

Will they ever go to sleep?

I CAN READ!™ with the BERENSTAIN BEARS

by Jan and Mike Berenstain

Phonics scope and sequence by Cathy Toohey

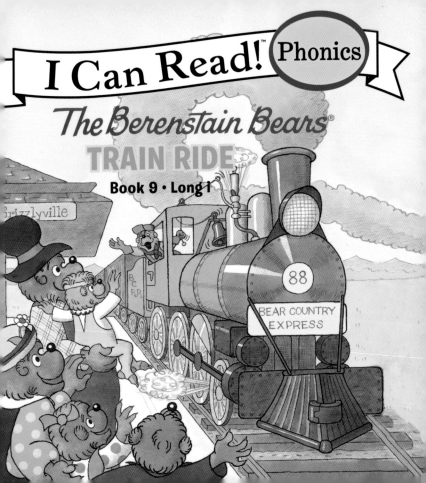

I Can Read! Phonics

The Berenstain Bears®
TRAIN RIDE
Book 9 • Long i

HOORAY!

_____

can read this book!

In this story, you will read or hear words with the **long i** vowel sound. Look for these words in the story and sound them out:

behind	by	drive
driver	excited	hi
inside	lights	outside
ride	shiny	signs
slide	time	tired

Here are some sight words:

are	here	look
looking	their	they
want		

Here are some fun Berenstain Bears words:

farm	house	school
town	train	woo-hoo

The cubs are excited.

They are going for a ride

on a train!

Woo-hoo!

The shiny train is here.

The driver waves hi.

It is time to go.

The Bears step inside.

The Bears look outside.

They ride by their house.

They ride by the farm.

They ride by town.

They see a slide behind a school.

They see cars and lights.

They see signs.

The cubs are tired of looking
outside.

They want to drive the train.

Woo-hoo!

I CAN READ!™ with the BERENSTAIN BEARS

by Jan and Mike Berenstain

Phonics scope and sequence by Cathy Toohey

HOORAY!

_____

can read this book!

In this story, you will read or hear words with the **long o** vowel sound. Look for these words in the story and sound them out:

alone	boats	cove
don't	go	gold
groans	hole	holes
home	hope	no
ocean	old	road
stones	trove	whole

Here are some sight words:

but	have	here
look	more	they

Here are some fun Berenstain Bears words:

beach	digs	map	Papa
pirates	play	treasures	

The Bears take a road to the beach.

Look at the boats!

Papa finds a map.

It's to Pirates Cove!

Will they find gold?

The cubs play in the ocean.

Papa digs a hole . . . alone!

Papa groans at the old shells and stones. No gold here.

Papa digs more holes, but
still no gold.
Don't lose hope, Papa.

Look, Papa!

The cubs have a whole trove of
treasures from the sea.

Now they can go home!

I CAN READ!™ with the BERENSTAIN BEARS

by Jan and Mike Berenstain

Phonics scope and sequence by Cathy Toohey

I Can Read! Phonics

The Berenstain Bears
MOO!
Book 11 • Long u and oo

HOORAY!

_____

can read this book!

In this story, you will read or hear words with the **long u** and **oo** (as in moo) vowel sounds. Look for these words in the story and sound them out.

long u:

blue	**cute**	**fruit**	**huge**	**phew**

long oo:

boo	**chew**	**coop**	**food**	**moo**
noon	**roof**	**scoop**	**shoos**	**spooky**
today	**too**			

Here are some sight words:

after	**are**	**away**	**by**	**comes**
for	**from**	**inside**	**very**	

Here are some fun Berenstain Bears words:

barn	**cock-a-doodle-doo**	**cows**
farm	**oink**	**pigs**	**scarecrow**

The Bears are visiting the farm today.
They see the red barn with the blue roof.

It's feeding time.

The cows chew their food.

Moo!

From inside the coop comes a loud cock-a-doodle-doo.
Inside, the hens eat scoop after scoop.

The pigs are huge from all the food.

But they are still very cute.

Oink!

Boo!

The spooky scarecrow shoos

away the crows.

Phew!

By noon the Bears are
hungry, too.
Lucky for them, there's lots
of fresh fruit!

I CAN READ!™ with the
BERENSTAIN BEARS

by Jan and Mike Berenstain

Phonics scope and sequence by Cathy Toohey

HOORAY!

_____

can read this book!

In this story, you will read or hear words with the long vowel sounds. Look for these words in the story and sound them out.

long a:

day   **great**   **hay**   **take**   **they**

long e:

clean   **each**   **feed**   **he**   **see**

long i:

like   **likes**   **prize**

ride   **riders**

long o:

blows   **nose**   **pony**   **show**

long u/oo:

cute   **hoof**   **too**

Here are some sight words:

every   **one**   **the**   **their**

The cubs like to take care
of the farm animals.

One day, they see a cute pony.
They pet his nose, and he
blows on their hands.
The pony likes the cubs.

The cubs clean the pony.

They feed him hay.

They scrape each hoof.

Great job, cubs!

The farmer lets the cubs ride

the pony.

The cubs begin to take
care of the pony every day.
They become great riders, too!

The cubs ride in a show.

They win a prize.

Hooray for the cubs!

Hooray for the cute pony!

I CAN READ!™ with the BERENSTAIN BEARS

by Jan and Mike Berenstain

Phonics scope and sequence by Cathy Toohey